Y0-BRG-581

Nelson Mandela
넬슨 만델라

Biography Comic
who? ⑰ Nelson Mandela

초판 1쇄 인쇄 2011년 4월 8일
초판 1쇄 발행 2011년 4월 15일

지은이 오영석
그린이 스튜디오 청비
번역 자넷 재완 신
감수 김수희
펴낸이 김선식

Chief Story Creator 김정미
Story Creator 채정은
Design Creator 김경민
Marketing Creator 신문수

Brand Creative Story Team 김정미, 채정은, 박혜연
Creative Design Dept. 최부돈, 황정민, 김태수, 조혜상, 이성희, 김경민
Creative Marketing Dept. 모계영, 이주화, 김하늘, 신문수
        Communication Team 서선행, 김선준, 박혜원, 전아름
        Contents Rights Team 이정순, 김미영
New Business Team 우재오
Creative Management Team 김성자, 김미현, 김유미, 정연주, 서여주, 권송이
Outsourcing 임나윤

펴낸곳 (주)다산북스
주소 서울시 마포구 서교동 395-27번지
전화 02-702-1724(기획편집) 02-703-1725(마케팅) 02-704-1724(경영지원)
팩스 02-703-2219
이메일 dasanbooks@hanmail.net
홈페이지 www.dasanbooks.com
출판등록 2005년 12월 23일 제313-2005-00277호

필름 출력 스크린그래픽센타 **종이** 월드페이퍼(주) **인쇄·제본** (주)현문

ISBN 978-89-6370-445-6 14740
SET 978-89-6370-438-8

who?

Nelson Mandela

넬슨 만델라

글 **오영석** | 그림 **스튜디오 청비** | 번역 **자넷 재완 신** | 감수 **김수희**

Dasan Kid

Nelson Mandela

South Africa's first black president, July 18, 1918 ~ present

Nelson Mandela was named Rolihlahla when he was born, which means "troublemaker." He was born in 1918 to the chief of the Thembu tribe of Umtata, South Africa. When he started going to school and receiving a white-centered education, he experienced racial discrimination for the first time. It was then that he was given the English name,

Nelson. In order to represent blacks who were being severely discriminated by whites and fight the unfair treatment of African people, Nelson started studying law. Unfortunately, due to his involvement in student movements, he was expelled from the school. He did not give up his dreams, and continued to prepare for his law studies as he worked at a law office.

In 1952, Mandela became the first black lawyer in South Africa, and opened up his own law office in Johannesburg. He gathered blacks and Asians together and declared a Freedom Charter to oppose racial discrimination. Mandela led many demonstrations and afterwards, traveled around Africa to speak about the situation in South Africa. Eventually, Mandela was arrested by the white police and sentenced to life in prison.

Mandela might have lost his freedom, but he did not stop working while in prison. He fought against the unjust violent treatment black prisoners were getting and led the way for improving the prison environment. Despite his status as a convicted prisoner, Mandela received human rights awards of every kind.

This had a great effect on the black citizens of South Africa. Blacks began to gather around the country and start black rights movements to support Mandela. The white government eventually surrendered and decided to release Mandela from prison.

After his release, he began to continue fighting for blacks' rights and forced the abolishment of the racial separation law that South Africa was known for, apartheid. He then became the first black president of South Africa. Despite his advanced age of over ninety, Nelson Mandela is currently still working on solutions for world peace and human rights issues.

넬슨 만델라

남아프리카 공화국 최초의 흑인 대통령, 1918년 7월 18일 ~

넬슨 만델라의 어릴 적 이름은 롤리 흘라흘라였습니다. '말썽꾸러기' 라는 뜻의 이 이름을 가진 아이는 1918년 남아프리카 공화국 움타타에서 템 부족 추장의 아들로 태어납니다. 그는 학교에 입학하여 백인 중심의 교육을 받게 되면서 처음으로 인종 차별을 경험합니다. 넬슨이라는 영어 이름을 갖게 된 것도 이 때였습니다.

넬슨은 백인들로부터 심각한 차별을 받고 있는 흑인들과 아프리카 민족들의 억울함을 대변하기 위해 법 공부를 시작하지만 학생운동을 하다가 퇴학을 당하고 맙니다. 하지만 그는 꿈을 포기하지 않았고, 법률 사무소에서 일하며 변호사가 되기 위한 준비를 계속하였습니다.

결국 넬슨 만델라는 1952년, 남아프리카 공화국 흑인 최초로 변호사가 되어 수도 요하네스버그에 법률 사무소를 엽니다. 그리고 흑인과 아시안계 인종들을 모아 인종 차별에 대항하는 자유 헌장을 선포합니다. 그는 여러 번의 시위를 주도 하였고 이후 아프리카를 순회하며 남아공의 현실을 알리는 데 힘씁니다. 결국 넬슨 만델라는 백인 경찰에 체포되어 종신형을 선고받고 맙니다.

감옥에 갇혀 자유를 잃었지만 그 속에서도 만델라의 활동은 멈추지 않았습니다. 흑인 죄수들에게 가해지던 부당한 대우에 맞서 싸웠고, 감옥의 환경을 개선하는 데에 앞장섰습니다. 그 공으로 죄수 신분임에도 불구하고 각종 인권 상을 수상하기에 이릅니다.

이런 일들은 남아프리카 공화국 흑인들에게 많은 영향을 주었습니다. 곳곳에서 만델라의 정신을 잇기 위한 흑인 인권 운동이 일어났고, 결국 이에 항복한 백인들은 만델라의 석방을 결정합니다.

감옥에서 나온 만델라는 다시 흑인 인권을 되찾기 위한 활동을 시작했고, 남아프리카 공화국의 대표적인 인종 파별법인 '아파르트헤이트'를 폐지시켰습니다. 그리고 흑인 최초로 남아프리카 공화국 대통령이 됩니다. 현재, 넬슨 만델라는 90살이 넘은 노령의 나이에도 불구하고 세계 평화와 인권 문제 해결을 위해 적극적인 활동을 이어가고 있습니다.

이 책을 만든 사람들

글 · 오영석

어린이들이 재미있고 신나게 읽을 수 있는 책을 쓰기 위해 노력하는 작가입니다. 나와 똑같이 고민하고, 실패했던 위인들의 이야기를 통해 독자들도 '할 수 있다'는 마음을 가지길 바랍니다. 작품으로 『세계사 한국사』, 『과학 교과 주제 탐구Q. 몸』, 『걸어서 세계 속으로 2. 일본』 등이 있습니다.

그림 · 스튜디오 청비

어린이들을 위해 새롭고, 재미있고, 즐거운 이야깃거리를 만드는 만화 창작 집단입니다. 세상을 바꾼 인물들의 삶을 통해 어린이들이 희망찬 미래를 만들어가길 바랍니다. 작품으로 『지식 똑똑 경제 리더십 탐구-긍정의 힘』, 『why? 서양 근대 사회의 시작』, 『why? 세계대전과 전후의 세계』 등이 있습니다. 이 책은 이준형 작가님이 그림을 그리셨습니다.

번역 · 자넷 재완 신(Janet Jaywan Shin)

미국 메릴랜드 주에서 태어나고 자랐습니다. 메릴랜드 대학교에서 언어학을 전공하고 UCLA에서 응용언어학 석사 학위를 취득했습니다. 서울대학교 언어교육원에서 전임 강사, 서울대학교 사범대학교 영어교육과에서 초빙교수로 일했습니다. 감수한 책으로 『서울대생한테 비밀 영어과외받기』가 있고 고등학교 영어 교과서 교정 작업에 참여했습니다.

감수 · 김수희

연세대학교에서 역사를 전공했습니다. 이후 한국뿐 아니라 일본, 미국에서 한국어, 일본어, 영어를 가르쳐 왔으며 부모를 위한 영어교육용 책을 썼습니다. 영어교육채널 EBSe '엄마표 영어특강'에서 강의를 하며 홈스쿨, 알파벳과 파닉스, 다차원 테마 영어 수업 기법을 알리고 있습니다. 전국 각지에서 어린이 영어 교육에 대한 강연을 하며 창의적이고 열정적인 교수법으로 영어를 배우고자 하는 어린이와 부모들에게 많은 도움을 주고 있습니다.

Nelson Mandela

Nelson Mandela became the first democratically elected President of _____ in 1994.

a. Australia
b. South Africa
c. France

Answer: b

Contents

African Royalty

01

Nelson Mandela was born on July 18, 1918, in a village called Mvezo, in the Umtata district of the Republic of South Africa.

When he was born, he was given the name, Rolihlahla, which means "to pull a branch off a tree," or also "troublemaker."

WAAAH

Nelson grew up with much love from his parents.

I'm number one!

Stay put, Rolihlahla!

Heh heh, I'm faster than you!

Why are you looking at me like that?

Because you look so grand.

Why?

All of the villagers respect you.

When you grow up, you will be respected, too. We are royalty, you know.

Royalty?

Really? If I become chief, then I'm going to lead the village people well, just like you.

That's right. Our family is Xhosa royalty. When you grow up, you too, will become chief of a tribe.

Is that right? How so?

Well, I don't know yet.

Look, Rolihlahla, at creation.

We are part of creation, together with Mother Earth and the animals, mingling and breathing together. You must never forget that.

I-I don't understand.

You will soon. As long as we respect nature and do not destroy the land, we are all brothers under Mother Earth.

Nelson's father was chief of the Thembu tribe. He was a burly handsome leader who drew the respect of all of the village people.

One day, an unwelcome visitor stopped by the peaceful village of Mvezo.

It was you. The one who disregarded the orders of the justice of the peace*.

Ah, you have come because of the incident involving one of the citizens who lost his cow. That will be taken care of in the tribal meeting.

Listen, darkie. That is for the courts to decide. You just follow our orders. If we say come, you come. If we say go, you go.

...

You'd better apologize!

What?

Father is royalty! Your attitude is unforgivable.

*justice of the peace: A judge who has the power to hold a summary trial, as well as the power of arrest, search, and seizure.

Contrary to Nelson's father's words of assurance that everything would be fine, the Mandela family lost everything.

They ended up losing all of their wealth and position and had to move to a small village called Qunu.

However, Nelson adjusted quickly to his new environment. He lived up to the meaning of his name, troublemaker, with his cheerful and optimistic personality.

Haha. If you come down like this, then you won't hurt your bottom.

THUMP

21

School?

Yes, he asked what we thought of sending Rolihlahla to school.

Let's send him. If he studies, it should help secure a better future for him.

COUGH

UGH!

But dear, are you alright?

I'm alright.

COUGH

COUGH

There's someone who's here for the first time. Rolihlahla!

Yes!

Your name is a bit long. Let me give you a British name that's easy to pronounce.

Nelson gained a new name and studied hard at school. Then suddenly, one day...

Nelson, wake up, quickly!

Wh-what is it?

Your father is... is...

Father, what's wrong?

Nel...son, you...

be...come... a great... person...

24

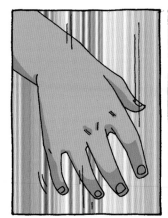

Dear? Father!

No!!!

FATHER!

Father, I promise that I'll reclaim our tribe once more.

After his father passed away, Nelson's family's financial situation became even more strained. Nelson's mother decided to send him away to live with the chief of a neighboring village, Jongintaba Dalindyebo.

Jongintaba was a man who became chief with the help of Nelson's father. He greeted Nelson with a warm heart.

Come on over. I've been waiting for you.

Nelson.

You know your father was an excellent chief, don't you?

Your father was a great help in my becoming chief of this tribe. So I want to return the favor to him.

I see.

We are one family. Call me Father from now on. My son Justice will be your brother.

Th-thank you.

Under Mother Earth, everyone is family. It's only natural to help one another, Nelson.

Oh!

As long as we respect nature and do not destroy the land, we are all brothers under Mother Earth.

Soon after Nelson began living with Jongintaba, there was a tribal meeting in the village.

...

You're here to watch the tribal meeting?

Yeah. I want to see how they decide on big issues.

This year, the grain harvest was not very good because of the drought. We must think about how to deal with this.

Isn't this something the chief should have prepared for in advance?

That's right. We must first discuss the qualifications of the chief.

What? Can farmers talk to the chief like that?

Nelson, have you forgotten Father's words? Under Mother Earth, we are all brothers, regardless of position.

But still, he's the chief.

Everyone's equal, whether chief or farmer, old or young.

There was no class discrimination in Jongintaba's tribal meeting. Nelson was deeply impressed when he saw the way they treated each other as complete equals in this meeting.

Thank you for all of your opinions.

It's getting late so we'll make our conclusions at the next tribal meeting.

Nelson, what are you doing here?

I wanted to watch the tribal meeting.

Man, I almost fell asleep.

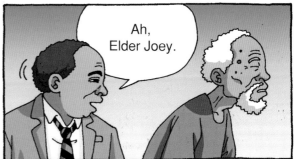

Legends?

Yes, I am talking about those brave, legendary heroes who fought lions and protected their tribes in battle.

Would you like to hear?

Nelson listened deep into the night to many stories about Africa's history and its heroes. This occasion planted a seed in Nelson's heart, a seed of tribal pride.

Under Jongintaba's care, Nelson grew up to become a healthy young man. He was now 16 years old.

I still can't believe it myself.

Nelson, you're finally becoming a man. Hahaha.

Once you go through the initiation ritual, you will be able to participate in the tribal meetings. And you will start your studies to become a future royal advisor.

Nelson, the initiation ritual speech is starting!

Go ahead.

Wow, everyone's already here!

Did you have to say that in your speech? These are boys who still have hope and dreams.

...

It's better to know the truth in advance than to find out too late and get discouraged.

...

Going to School

02

CD Track 15 ▶

After Nelson completed the initiation ritual, he began attending school to formally take classes about royal advising. The name of the school was Clarkesbury Boarding Institute.

This is a real...

...school built by white people.

How great it would be if people back home could enjoy this kind of life?

41

45

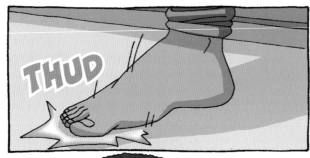

Wha-?
Look at
his outfit!

Everyone,
listen well.

Today we have a special
speech from Mqhayi, the poet
who wrote the national anthem
of the Republic of
South Africa.

I stand
before you
today as a
proud African.

Students, we Africans had established a great civilization. Every tribe lived under Mother Earth as brothers. We were one with nature and lived in harmony with the animals who roamed the land.

But then one day, people with white skin, carrying weapons that spewed out fire, destroyed our civilization.

What?

Oh!

Ah!

And this is what they said. This land originally had no civilization. We have given you black people a civilization, for which you should be grateful.

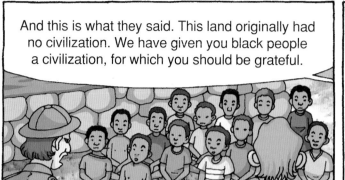

They demolished our property and began to build buildings made of cement. They even shot and killed the animals we had been harmoniously living with.

Stop! Stop!

Students, we cannot let these foreigners who do not cherish our culture or history take our land away from us.

WOOOSH

We must restore our wonderful history and culture. We must stand up once again!

03

Nelson Madela, the College Student

 Track 21 ▶

In 1940, 21-year-old Nelson entered a school established for blacks, Fort Hare University.

Hi, I'm Paul Mahabane. You're Nelson, the Xhosa, right?

Yeah, that's right.

Unlike students who were active in the black movement, Nelson was devoted solely to his studies. One day, he was on his way to buy a book he needed for class.

CLINK

CLINK

ROLL...

!

Come on! Aren't you going to pick it up?

I don't do errands for whites.

What? Do you know who I am?

Well, you must be one of the whites who think they're better than everyone else in the world.

Let's go, Nelson.

A-alright.

Grrrr!

Nelson, you went to the bookstore yesterday, didn't you?

Yes, sir.

I heard you were with someone of very poor character. Paul Mahabane.

He's not a bad person. A white man was just trying to ask us to do an errand for him.

Oh no, you're already being influenced by him. He is a corrupt student who is a member of the ANC. Aren't you of the royal Xhosa lineage?

Don't associate with students like him. And also,

...

you should be grateful when a white person asks you to do an errand.

The fact that he's asking you means you're getting recognition from a white man, wouldn't you agree?

Recognition?

It's an honor for a black person. So just do whatever you're told to do.

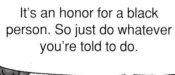

Oh, and you know the student body election is coming up? I can appoint you to be the student body president if you follow my orders as you're doing now and don't cause any trouble.

!

Oh yeah? So you're saying all blacks need to do is to obey whites? I'm going to turn that thinking around completely!

Anyone want to join a movement not to vote in the student elections?

What are you talking about?

Not vote?

The student council just does whatever the university wants it to do. It doesn't even consider what students think or want.

So you're saying you want to make a student council that works on behalf of the students, not one that works on behalf of the school?

It won't be easy to change.

We're gonna give it a try!

Let's reject the student elections and stand up for our rights!

I'm for it!

The student council should no longer be the puppet of white professors. The student elections need to be postponed!

Secure the power of the student council! We're not going to follow the orders of whites anymore!

These black lowlifes! Arrest them all!

This way!

Hurry!

Oh no!

Aah!

You lowlifes!

BAM

POW

KA-POW

POW

How dare you!

...

Nelson, this was unexpected. Has hanging out with Paul influenced you?

No. This was my decision. We are no longer going to have a student council that merely obeys the orders of the white professors.

That is very dangerous thinking. Look, blacks are stupid and uncivilized. Therefore, they can't make decisions for themselves.

That is not true.

I thought you were a good, submissive black boy, but now I see that you're an evil black boy who riles up the good students.

You're expelled from this school!

Professor, that's not right.

Pack your bags and leave at once!

Oh!

Nelson was forced to return to Jongintaba's hometown after getting expelled from the university.

Tell me what happened. You got expelled?

I'm sorry to disappoint you.

Ahh, what has happened has happened. Let's do this then.

I'm old and weary now. I need someone to take my place. I want you to stay here with me.

What do you mean?

I'll give you one village to lead. Stay here and be an advisor to our tribe.

I'm too young. I'm not even married.

So I want to arrange a marriage for you.

Excuse me?

I've already chosen a bride for you.

I'm still...

...

Sigh, what do I do?

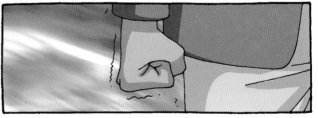

I'm sorry. I'm too young to stay behind in the village.

One day, I'll repay you for taking me in and raising me like a real son. Please take care.

Nelson left Jongintaba's village and went to Johannesburg, the capital of South Africa. There, he worked in the mines.

CLING

CLANG

CLANG

CLING

04 In Johannesburg

 Track 28 ▶

While Nelson was working in the mines in Johannesburg, he heard about a successful man named Walter Sisulu. He went to meet Sisulu at his real estate office.

I'm looking for a man named Walter Sisulu.

65

The office Sisulu introduced Nelson to was the Witkin, Sidelsky, and Eidelman Law Office. It was one of the relatively larger law firms in Johannesburg.

There, Nelson was responsible for various miscellaneous tasks such as organizing papers, making tea, and throwing away the trash.

Nelson, throw this away.

Nelson, make me some coffee.

Newbie! Can't you move any faster?

Yes, sir. I'm coming!

Whew.

Tough first day, huh? Let's go eat lunch.

One day, Nelson was waiting for the bus on his way to do an errand for the law firm at the library.

Blackie, this bus is for whites only. The next bus is for blacks.

RUMBLE

CLUNK

CLUNK

If you're not gonna get on, get outta the way!

When Nelson arrived at the library, he went to the reading room to find the book he needed.

What do you think you're doing, blackie?

I'm going to read.

Blackies can't sit on the chairs. Think about it. Do you think a white person will want to sit on a chair that a black person has sat on? Disgusting!

Excuse me?!

What kind of look is that? Are you challenging me? You wanna get dragged out?

!

The racial discrimination he faced while working was quite harsh. Nelson's days were full of difficulties.

Huh? Mr. Sisulu, what are you doing here?

Nelson, did you hear the news?

They announced that the bus fare has been raised 25%.

25%?

That's right. Now blacks might spend up to a quarter of their wages on bus fare.

Sigh. I'm already walking ten kilometers every day because I don't have the money to buy a bus ticket.

Right. They're not paying blacks fair wages, either. It's really terrible.

Is there anything we can do about it?

I'm organizing a demonstration to protest the bus fare price hike. It's basically a movement to not ride the buses. Do you want to participate?

Of course. I'll participate!

Yeah, I knew you would.

Following the blacks' protest, the government officials held a meeting.

*riot: Disrupting order in society by instigating group violence.

The demonstration against the bus fare increase was successful. This was a major turning point in Nelson's life when he realized that the power of blacks united together could change the world.

Black Liberation Movement

05

Nelson went to visit the ANC office. The ANC was an organization which protected the rights of black Africans. They generally used nonviolent means to lobby for blacks' rights to the white government.

I'd like to introduce you to a new friend!

Hello.

Oh, I was wondering who it was. It's Nelson!

Do you know me?

Aren't you the one who organized the movement at Fort Hare University to reject the student elections? I was there too. I'm Oliver Tambo.

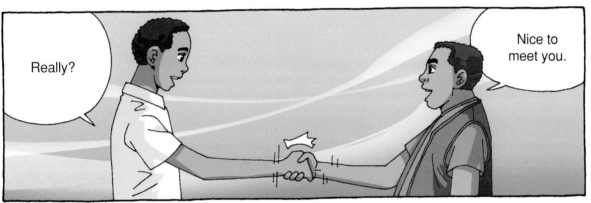

Really?

Nice to meet you.

Now I can see that you're not an ordinary fellow. Why don't you say a few words to introduce yourself to your new comrades?

Alright.

...

I realized recently that when blacks work together, we can change the world. I wanted to get more involved in the black movement, so I decided to officially join the ANC.

Welcome, brother.

But it seems to me that ANC is not doing enough to secure real freedom for blacks.

What are you talking about?

The ANC needs to work more aggressively than it's doing now. The Black rights movement so far has been too passive.

Because of its nonviolent approach, the ANC was a unifying organization accepted by many African blacks. In 1944, Nelson created a youth league within the ANC. It served to more aggressively fight for blacks' freedom and rights without compromising the principles of the ANC to use peaceful methods.

Nelson did not neglect his law studies which would enable him to fulfill his dream.

Then in 1952, he passed the bar exam and finally opened a law office with his friend Oliver Tambo. This was a first for blacks.

Nelson, I can't believe you passed the bar exam!

My dream has finally come true! Now I can help our people much more.

The office that Nelson established was enormously popular with blacks. To blacks who had to endure abuse from whites but had no knowledge of the law and could not demand their proper rights on their own, a black lawyer was practically a savior.

Mandela and Tambo

However, white people did not acknowledge the legitimacy of a black lawyer.

What freedom or rights do blackies have?

Lawyer, huh? I don't believe it.

We can't let them continue.

THWACK

Ack!

What is this?

THWACK

BANG

Ugh!

The whites are attacking!

Everybody, run!

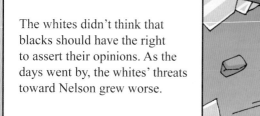

The whites didn't think that blacks should have the right to assert their opinions. As the days went by, the whites' threats toward Nelson grew worse.

Nelson, we'd better move our office to another location.

Ugh! You think we can get outta here?

So the office is completely destroyed?

Yes. So next week, we plan to move to a black neighborhood.

It's terrible. The world is becoming a difficult place for blacks to live in as each day passes.

Oh yeah. Did you hear that the black education bill passed?

Yes, I heard. I guess that means schools that admit blacks have to close down.

...

That's not all. The discrimination against Indians and Asians has gotten harsher, too. It's becoming a white man's world completely.

Apartheid is gaining momentum all around society.

South Africa went ahead with its apartheid policy which consisted of laws legalizing discrimination against blacks. Apartheid, which means to separate, was a policy which kept blacks and whites separate.

The white government ranked people according to four racial categories, the lowest rank being blacks.

White people considered it a disgrace to live together with blacks, who were considered of lowest worth. Consequently, they designated an area for blacks to live in and forced them all to move there.

In the end, blacks, who comprise 80% of the South African population, had to move to a small, cramped area a little over 10% of the entire land.

Get in there! I said get in there!

Blacks went to schools designated for blacks and they could only enter professions which had already been determined.

Blacks are not allowed to work at our company.

...

In addition, blacks did not have to right to participate in politics. This is how blacks in South Africa got all of their rights as citizens taken away.

I heard the presidential election is coming up.

It doesn't matter to us since it's the white people who vote.

This is a good opportunity for us. Other people who face discrimination besides blacks might want to come to our meetings.

Yeah, if all colored people unite and work together, we can make our intent clear to them.

How can we do this?

By going on strike.

Strike?

This country's economy won't be able to function if blacks stop working. If all blacks refuse to work, the whites will be helpless.

That's a great idea! Let's first meet with the tribal leaders.

Under Nelson's leadership, representatives of South Africa's colored people gathered together.

Everyone, listen! The government is making their racial segregation policy stronger and they are suppressing us.

We cannot live this way like slaves to white people!

So today we are going to read the Freedom Charter and conduct a demonstration to get the attention of the white government. I urge you all to participate!

Freedom Charter! We, the People of South Africa, declare for all our country and the world to know:

The rights of the people shall be the same, regardless of race, color, or sex.

However the government has separated us by race and discriminates against us. Therefore, we present the following demands!

Every man and woman shall have the right to vote, regardless of skin color. The national wealth of our country, the heritage of South Africans, shall be restored to the people.

With no racial discrimination, equal legal rights shall be given to all! The right to enjoy work, home, peace, and security for all!

As citizens of a democratic nation, we adopt the Freedom Charter and pledge to fight until this nation becomes a true democracy.

Freedom Charter!

Blacks and whites are equal citizens!

As the Freedom Charter Nelson was advocating became known, blacks all over society began to take group action.

Do Away with Apartheid Policy!

We are Citizens just like Whites!

What is this?

Are you all insane? Get back to work!

WHACK

WHACK

Don't hit! We are humans, too!

What? You dare to talk back?

Nelson came up with another plan to show whites what blacks were concerned about. They would disrupt the 300th anniversary celebration of Europeans' settlement in South Africa.

You know, right? Today is a celebration day for the whites.

It's been 300 years since Europeans first set foot on this land. Is that something to celebrate?

Let's let them know once and for all.

Blacks continued to fight even after Nelson was arrested. Somehow they caught onto Nelson's passion and realized that they themselves had to take action in order for society to change.

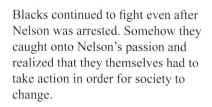

The South African government was at a loss for what to do about the blacks' demonstrations which began with Nelson's Freedom Charter.

Doesn't that mean that we've given in to them? We cannot do that. We must find another way.

There is one way.

What is it? Tell us.

We use guns against the protesters.

Then they'd run and disperse out of fear.

Guns? What if some people died as a result?

Sir, are the lives of blackies worth that much?

...

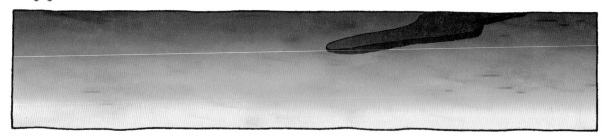

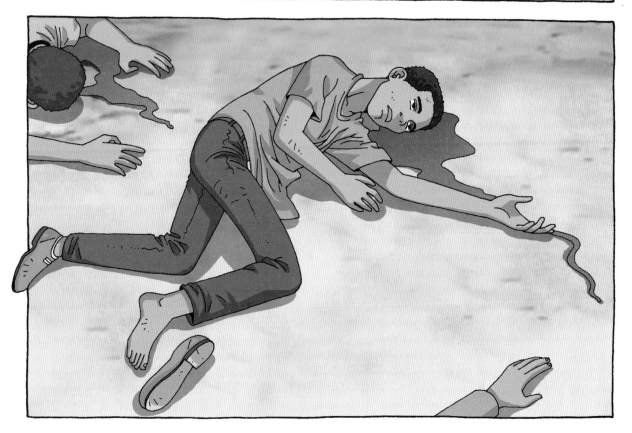

The Sharpeville massacre. White policemen fired randomly at black demonstrators, resulting in 70 deaths and 180 injuries.

Nelson had been charged with threatening the government with the Freedom Charter he was advocating. He went to trial and was found not guilty, and then released.

Mandela!

It's great you're out unharmed.

I heard about the Sharpeville incident while I was in jail.

It was horrible. So we stopped conducting demonstrations after that.

How could they just shoot at innocent citizens?

Let's go and work on a counter plan.

I've already made up my mind.

There is no hope in a country which shoots its own citizens. We must also engage in an armed battle*.

Armed battle?

We need a new organization. I will make one.

Nelson believed that nonviolent methods only put blacks' lives in danger. Later, Nelson formed an organization called Umkhonto we Sizwe, meaning "'spear of the nation," which would confront the South African government armed with weapons.

Spear of the Nation
Umkhonto we Sizwe

Right. We can't do it with our own strength. Have a productive trip.

Mr. Sisulu, please take care of this new organization. I will travel to other countries to inform people of the situation here and gather their support.

After some time, Nelson traveled outside of South Africa as a representative for "Spear of the Nation."

*armed battle: Fighting with physical strength or armed forces.

Nelson traveled to various countries to let the world know about the situation blacks faced in South Africa.

Everyone around the world paid attention to this black activist from South Africa.

One year had passed since then, when one day...

Aren't you Nelson Mandela?

Who are you?

I came on behalf of Mr. Sisulu. Disguise yourself with these.

Thank you.

There's a bus over there. You're going to pretend to be the bus driver and drive to Johannesburg.

Heh heh

VROOM...

Mandela, we know it's you.

SCREEE

SCREEE

Come out nice and slow!

Gasp!

06 · 27 Years in Prison

 Track 49 ▶

Your Honor, Mandela is a wayward man who has participated in a movement to reject the student elections at Fort Hare University and also a movement in Johannesburg to protest the bus fare increase.

In addition, he created the Freedom Charter which opposes the policies of the government and he is responsible for leading blacks' strikes and demonstrations.

Recently, he has formed an organization which resists the government with military force. Also, he has been traveling to other countries and speaking against South Africa's government.

Nelson Mandela has resisted the government and disgraced the name of South Africa around the world. We demand that he be declared guilty of national treason* and receive the death penalty.

*treason: The act of betraying one's country and people and attempting to take away the governing power of the ruler.

107

Your Honor, the one who should stand trial here is not me, but the white government of South Africa.

This country's government makes laws which solely benefit white people, exploits black people, and creates discrimination between human beings. They must pay for their sins.

...

I followed my conscience to help South Africa, the nation that I love, become a democratic nation where all people are equal.

...

If a government uses force on its citizens, then conversely, citizens can use force against the government. We were fighting for our very lives.

I will continue to fight until there is freedom, equality, and true democracy in South Africa. If need be, I am willing to die for this cause.

Oh!

...

Sir, Mandela went on trial yesterday.

And the verdict?

The verdict will be announced at the next trial. And this is Mandela's final statement.

Hmm...

Don't let Mandela's speech in the courtroom reach the media. If blacks see this, they will rise up again.

Yes, sir.

When Nelson and like-minded black leaders emerged, the South African government became nervous. If blacks, who outnumbered the white population by a ratio of 8 to 1, started to riot, things would quickly get out of control.

Everyone, listen up!

You are not to publish Mandela's final statement in the paper! If you do, we are closing down this newspaper.

...

Have you all thought about what we should do with Mandela?

Sir, we have to execute him. If the blacks have a leader like Mandela, they will gather again and create a nationwide riot.

The blacks' movements are serious now, too. And Mandela is in the center of it all.

110

If that's the case, we'd better nip it in the bud. Death penalty for...

Sir, Mandela's final statement has been published! Internationally, too!

Wh-what?

Internationally?

Despite South Africa's careful crackdown, Nelson's final statement became known all around the world.

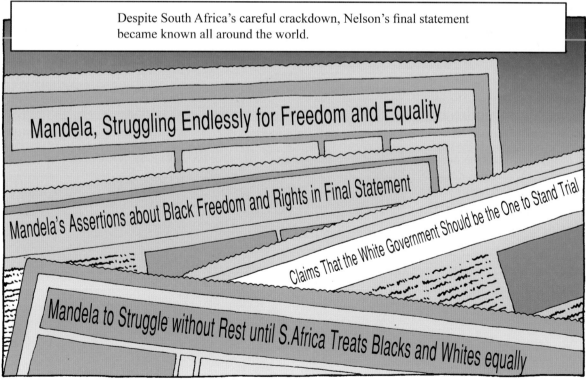

Mandela, Struggling Endlessly for Freedom and Equality

Mandela's Assertions about Black Freedom and Rights in Final Statement

Claims That the White Government Should be the One to Stand Trial

Mandela to Struggle without Rest until S.Africa Treats Blacks and Whites equally

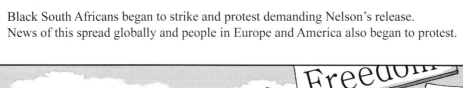

Black South Africans began to strike and protest demanding Nelson's release.
News of this spread globally and people in Europe and America also began to protest.

With the world criticizing the South African government, the government officials were in a bind about how to handle Nelson. If they executed Nelson, they could be criticized by people all over the world.

Nelson suddenly became a figure who had the support of all the citizens of South Africa and the entire world.

*Life imprisonment: Punishment of spending one s entire life in prison.

Nelson was sent to a prison on Robben Island. This prison was rumored to be especially harsh to black prisoners.

Put it on!

I will not wear this. This is children's clothing. Don't treat black people like children.

What? You don't have the right to choose. Put it on, now!

I refuse.

What's this?

Let's stop here. If you mess with Mandela, you'll have to deal with us.

You...

Thank you for coming to my aid.

No problem, sir.

The blacks here all know who you are.

They know me?

And you all showed your bravery by standing up to that guard.

HA HA HA

You wrote the Freedom Charter and led demonstrations.

And you even risked your life and traveled overseas to let the whole world know about our situation.

While Nelson was in prison, the black rights movement became more intense. If the government used force against its citizens, its citizens would use force too, just as Mandela had said.

Don't retreat!

We will keep resisting!

Hey, blackie! Come here and clean up this trash.

Blacks were coming to their senses in everyday life as well. They now recognized when they were being discriminated against and understood that that was wrong.

I don't follow a white man's orders.

You...

Resistance and clashes continued until 1990, resulting in a massacre of three million black South Africans by the white government.

Blackies! So now you're not scared of anything, huh?

We're humans, too. We're not gonna just take it!

This kind of situation in South Africa required international regulation.

What? How?

Killing millions of innocent Africans. From now on, an embargo will be imposed on all of South Africa's trade.

Flights going to South Africa one by one were cancelled, preventing South Africa from participating in the Olympics or the World Cup that year.

This nation's whites have no right to ride on an airplane.

South Africa will not be allowed to participate in any international events.

This rejection from the rest of the world continued, and South Africa's government began to seriously consider what to do about the black situation.

Meanwhile, Nelson was encountering discrimination in jail.

I would like to read a book. Could you bring me one?

What? Why does a blackie need a book for?

Nelson, what book do you want to read? I'll get it for you.

Chief!

Prison Head Office

Chief, why are you treating Mandela well?

While in prison, Nelson received the support of his fellow inmates and faced the discrimination from the guards. His efforts were recognized internationally and he received various human rights awards while in prison.

When people involved in the black rights movement heard about Nelson being given human rights awards, they were moved.

Look at this! Mandela got another award. Even in prison, he's fighting discrimination from the guards.

That's Mandela. He might be in jail, but they haven't crushed his great spirit!

Nelson's body might have been in jail but his reputation was spreading far and wide. Black people in society would sometimes talk about how things would be if Nelson weren't imprisoned.

Have you heard? Mandela's teaching his fellow black prisoners how to read and write.

I heard he got them to change the black prisoners' short pants uniforms to long pants.

And he went on a hunger strike to improve the black prisoners' meals.

He's doing all that while he's a prisoner. Imagine how much he'd be doing if he were free.

The atmosphere in prison slowly began to change. Black prisoners would gather around Nelson to share stories of freedom and hope.

Though our bodies are not free, each of our minds has hot embers hidden inside.

And the guards no longer treated the blacks as roughly as they used to. A few guards were even quite friendly with Nelson who had created peaceful order among the black prisoners.

The mood here has improved so much because of you, Mandela.

Hahaha. Well, it's because everyone has been working together.

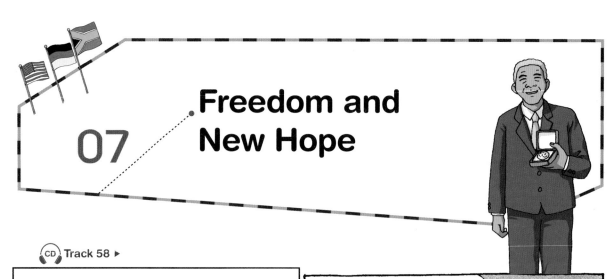

07 Freedom and New Hope

25 years had passed since Nelson had been imprisoned. Then suddenly one day, a government official came to meet with Nelson.

CREAK...

Mr. Mandela, you've received many awards while you've been in prison.

Yes, I'm very thankful.

South Africa is getting a lot of international pressure. The reason is because great people like you, who are receiving awards even while in prison, are being suppressed.

So the South African government is yielding to this international pressure and planning to abolish its apartheid policy.

124

On February 11, 1990, Nelson became a free man after 27 years in prison. Mandela the young man had at some point turned into a white-haired grandfather.

How long has it been? It's like a dream!

Nelson, did you hear that the President wants to meet with you?

Yes, I am going to take this opportunity to talk to him about blacks' rights.

Yes, international pressure is strong so the government will listen to your requests.

Meanwhile, the white people had been enjoying their power and became nervous once Nelson was released.

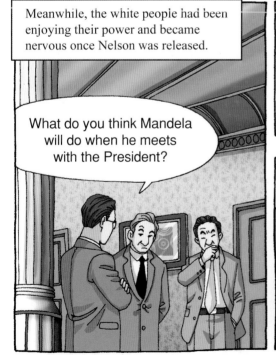

What do you think Mandela will do when he meets with the President?

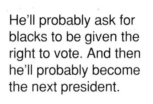

He'll probably ask for blacks to be given the right to vote. And then he'll probably become the next president.

And we'll get kicked out of our offices.

Hmm.

While dining with President F.W. de Klerk, Nelson talked about the racial discrimination that weighed down on him and blacks in South Africa.

As a representative of blacks and colored people, I have a proposal I would like to make to the government.

Give blacks the right to vote. 82 percent of the population of South Africa is black. But they have never once been able to directly choose their own president.

Hmm.

128

But that means we have to change the Constitution. It will take a long time.

If you cannot meet our demands, we will conduct a large-scale civil rights movement. We will let it be known throughout the world that the South African government has still not truly abolished its racial segregation policy.

I will do my best.

But what I'm worried about is...

Yes?

If blacks participate in the elections, you will probably become the next president, Mr. Mandela. Then don't you think the blacks who obtain power will take revenge on whites?

129

I will make you a promise right here.

Every citizen in South Africa, regardless of skin color, religion, or gender, will have the same rights.

Whites are also South African brothers, and citizens.

Soon a great change arose in South Africa.

Dear citizens of South Africa,

Beginning today, the apartheid policy will be abolished.

Presidential elections will be held soon, and blacks will be able to participate.

131

In 1993, Nelson together with de Klerk was awarded the Nobel Peace Prize for their work of abolishing the apartheid policy in South Africa.

On April 27, 1994, South Africa held its first election since apartheid was abolished. South African blacks earnestly wanted Nelson Mandela to become president. At some point, Nelson had become a hero to them, having made the Freedom Charter and fought for blacks' rights before being sent to prison for 27 years.

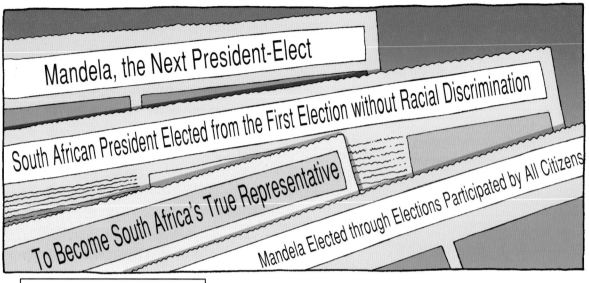

Mandela, the Next President-Elect

South African President Elected from the First Election without Racial Discrimination

To Become South Africa's True Representative

Mandela Elected through Elections Participated by All Citizens

On May 10, 1994, an event in Pretoria, South Africa would leave a mark in history.

I consider it an honor to be able to share this historical moment with all of you.

I introduce to you, the new President of the Republic of South Africa!

Nelson Mandela!

God bless Africa!

The first black president of South Africa, Nelson Mandela.

YEAH

Mandela!

Mandela!

YAY

YAY

With a strong will and firm beliefs, he spent his whole life fighting for the abolishment of racial discrimination. Nelson suffered under the suppression of whites but after he became president, he embraced them.

After Nelson completed his term as president, he returned to his hometown. There, he continues to confront unjust discrimination in different places around the world even today. The spirit of freedom and equality that he invested his whole life into will continue to be passed on.

SOUTH
AFRICA
2010

Word Search

● Find the words which are hidden horizontally, vertically and diagonally.

```
D I S C H A R G E M Z G Q Q M Z G Q M P
W S X N V E N T I O N H W W N A H W N A
E B Q J A B Q J E T B V R B A R I O B R
R V C K R D C K R V C K E R V C K N V T
E C W U R S E N T C D L T R C D U P C I
V R O Y A L T Y R X E Q Y Y D E N O X C
E Z V W U D V W C Z V W T U Z I J R Z I
A N A E I A E E I A R E E I A R C T A P
L S I R O S G C O S T R C O S G S T S A
P D C A P D H T O U H E O P D H T N D T
A F A Y H F U Y A P U Y V A F U Y I F E
N G S U S T I N C P I G E I N G U T G R
C H S I D H M I D R O I R D H O I Y H A
E J A B S O R A F E T J F F J T J F J W
S K N B G K R E R S P I E N T S B G K C
T L A N H L E N H S E N H H L E N H L E
O Q T M J Q T A U T D O R I T Y M J B T
R W E Q L W Y Q L M I S T R E A T L U Y
Z W K F Z W K F Z W K F Z Z S U F T Y R
X E M E M B A R G O I P A L E M U X N M
C R Q C C R Q C P C I G H T R Q C C R Q
```

ancestor	discharge	embargo	verdict
mistreat	royalty	suppress	participate

Vocabulary

● Match each word to the correct meaning.

1. liberation   • 대표

2. abolish   • 폐지하다

3. massacre   • 해방

4. representative   • 대학살

5. apartheid   • 충돌

6. constitution   • 남아공의 인종 차별 정책

7. segregation   • 인종차별

8. imprison   • 헌법

9. convict   • 폭동

10. clash   • 종신형

11. life imprisonment • 투옥하다

12. riot   • 유죄를 선고하다

Guess What?

● Guess what he said in the blank.

Africa Map

There are 53 countries and about 1 billion people in Africa.

Africa Facts

1. Africa is the second-largest continent on Earth, covering about 30,330,000 sq km. It is about three times the size of the United States.

2. Africa is considered to be where human beings first evolved.

3. Africa is home to some of Earth's most extraordinary animals like the African elephant which is the world's largest land animal, the giraffe which is the world's tallest animal, and the cheetah which is the world's fastest animal. There are also penguins in South Africa.

4. Africa is nearly surrounded on all sides by water, bordering the Atlantic Ocean to the west, the Indian Ocean to the east, and the Mediterranean to the north. The Atlantic and Indian Oceans meet to border Africa to the south.

5. Africa has rainforests, grasslands and deserts, but no huge mountain ranges.

6. The highest mountain in Africa is Mt. Kilimanjaro in Tanzania. Its Uhuru Point is 5895 m high.

7. The Sahara is the world's largest desert, nearly the size of the United States. And it is expanding southwards at an average of 0.8 km a month.

8. The Nile is the longest river in the world, at 6,650 km. It is formed from the Blue Nile which originates at Lake Tana in Ethiopia, and the White Nile which originates at Lake Victoria.

탄자니아에 있는 사바나 ©eismcsquare

리비아 서쪽에 있는 사하라 사막 ©Luca Galuzzi

9. Lake Victoria is the largest lake in Africa, and is the world's second largest freshwater lake covering an area of 69,490 sq km.

10. Lake Tanganyika is the deepest lake in Africa reaching at its greatest depth 1,436 m. It is the second deepest freshwater lake in the world after Lake Baikal.

11. The largest country in Africa is Sudan, and the smallest country is Seychelles.

12. The most populated country in Africa is Nigeria with a poplulation of more than 113 million.

13. The largest city in Africa is Cairo, the capital of Egypt.

14. South Africa has 3 capitals: Cape Town(legislative), Pretoria(administrative), Bloemfontein(judicial). But the most important economic, industrial, and cultural center of South Africa is Johannesburg.

15. South Africa has six Nobel Prize winners, which is more than most other countries.

    Albert J. Luthuli : Nobel Prize for Peace in 1960

    Aaron Klug : Nobel Prize for Chemistry in 1982

    Bishop Desmond Tutu : Nobel Prize for Peace in 1984

    Nadine Gordimer : Nobel Prize for Literature in 1991

    Nelson Mandela and Frederik W. de Klerk : Nobel Prize for peace in 1993

    John Maxwell Coetzee : Nobel Prize for Literature in 2003

1918년 남아프리카 공화국 움타타에서 템 부족 추장 가들라의 아들로 태어났습니다.

1934년 16세 클라크베리 중등학교에 입학해 백인 중심의 교육을 받습니다.

1940년 22세 포트헤어 대학에서 법학 공부를 하지만 학생 운동에 참여하다가 퇴학당합니다.

1941년 23세 결혼을 피해 요하네스버그로 향합니다.
월터 시술루의 소개로 법률 사무소에서 일합니다.

1944년 26세 월터 시술루, 올리버 탐보와 함께 아프리카 민족 회의(ANC) 안에 청년 동맹을 창설합니다.

1948년 30세 남아프리카 공화국에 인종 차별 정책인 아파르트헤이트가 본격적으로 시행됩니다.

1952년 34세 백인이 아닌 인종으로는 처음으로 변호사가 되어 요하네스버그에 법률 사무소를 열었습니다.

1955년 37세 만델라의 주도로 흑인과 아시안계 인종들이 모여 인종주의에 대항하는 자유헌장을 선포합니다.

1960년 42세 집회 중, 흑인들과 백인 경찰이 충돌하여 수백 명의 사상자를 낸 샤프빌 학살이 발생합니다.

1961년 43세 무장 투쟁 조직 '국민의 창'이 창설되고 만델라가 지휘를 맡습니다.

1962년	44세	2월, 아프리카를 순회하며 남아공의 현실을 알립니다. 8월, 남아프리카 공화국으로 돌아오던 중 경찰에 체포됩니다.
1964년	46세	종신형을 선고받고 로벤 섬 감옥에 수감됩니다.
1979년	61세	인권 부문에 대한 공로로 자와할랄네루상을 수상합니다.
1981년	63세	브루노 크라이스키 인권상을 수상합니다.
1983년	65세	유네스코 시몬 볼리바 국제상을 수상합니다.
1989년	71세	카다피 인권상을 수상합니다.
1990년	72세	2월 11일, 27년 만에 석방됩니다. 8월, 백인 정부와 인종 차별에 대해 협상합니다.
1991년	73세	인종 차별법인 아파르트헤이트 정책이 철폐됩니다.
1993년	75세	만델라와 데 클레르크가 공동으로 노벨 평화상을 수상합니다.
1994년	76세	4월 27일, 남아프리카 공화국 최초로 흑인이 참여하는 대통령 선거가 실시됩니다. 5월 10일, 남아프리카 공화국 대통령에 임명됩니다.
1999년	81세	대통령 임기를 마치고 정계를 은퇴합니다.
~현재		세계 평화와 인권 문제에 대해 관심을 가지고 국제적인 활동을 이어가고 있습니다.